Brian Ogden was for many years a teacher and RE advisor for the dioceses of Pet
author of more than 50 books, including many titles in the Barnabas range. These ir......
Assemblies, *Starting Together*, *Nursery Rhyme Nativities*, *Beyond the Candle Flame* and *Sing a Song of Seasons*.
Brian is a regular speaker in schools, preaches in the North Norfolk Methodist circuits and is grandfather to ten grandchildren.

Our EASTER PLAY

An easy-to-perform nursery rhyme play for Easter

Brian Ogden

Text copyright © Brian Ogden 2009
Illustrations copyright © Marie Allen 2009
The author asserts the moral right
to be identified as the author of this work

Published by
The Bible Reading Fellowship
15 The Chambers, Vineyard
Abingdon OX14 3FE
United Kingdom
Tel: +44 (0)1865 319700
Email: enquiries@brf.org.uk
Website: www.brf.org.uk

ISBN 978 1 84101 466 1
First published 2009
10 9 8 7 6 5 4 3 2 1 0

Acknowledgments
Unless otherwise stated, scripture quotations are taken from the Contemporary English Version of the Bible
published by HarperCollins Publishers, copyright © 1991, 1992, 1995 American Bible Society.

A catalogue record for this book is available from the British Library

Printed in Singapore by Craft Print International Ltd

CONTENTS

INTRODUCTION

Our Easter Play is an easily produced play for use with Foundation/Reception and Key Stage One pupils. The Easter story is seen through the experiences of Jesus' disciple Peter, although the narrative is carried by an adult narrator. The play introduces the events of Maundy Thursday, Good Friday and Easter Day, ending with the story of Jesus meeting with his disciples after the resurrection and preparing breakfast for them on the shores of Lake Galilee.

THE NARRATION

In the play, the story is recounted through narration, mime and singing. It cannot be emphasised too strongly that the narration is one of the most important features of the play. There may be a temptation to entrust it to a 'good reader' but, more often than not, even 'good readers' cannot be heard, and the presentation will be spoiled by inaudible narration. For this reason, it is essential that an adult acts as narrator.

THE PRESENTATION

Easter is a time of year when a special celebration is appropriate. The play may be used as part of a whole school presentation, as a class or year group assembly, as a school production with parents and visitors present, or as a celebration in church. The songs may be used on their own as a part of other assemblies during the season of Easter. This is a good way of learning them and teaching them to other children.

THE SONGS

The four songs are all written to popular tunes, and children will learn the songs very quickly.

All the words and music carry permission to photocopy, so there is no problem in providing the words of the songs to all attending any sort of performance. The participation of the audience is a vital and enjoyable aspect of the play, which both encourages the children and helps to generate a sense of sharing in the experience. In some places, in addition to the scripted songs, it is suggested that seasonal songs or recorded music are used.

THE CHILDREN

Schools come in different sizes! *Our Easter Play* is designed for use with either large or small numbers of children. Older children may be formed into a supporting choir. Younger children can mime the drama as indicated by the narration.

STAGING

The word 'stage' has been used throughout to indicate the acting area. If possible, there should be access from either side. All movement is given in the stage directions, which are shown in italics.

COSTUMES AND PROPS

Decisions over the use of costumes and props must be made locally, but the safety of the children is of prime importance. Traditional biblical costume can be suggested through the provision of pieces of fabric, dressing-up items, simple cord belts and so on. The two friezes or collages can be organised as a class project, using large sheets of sugar paper or lengths of paste-free lining wallpaper and paint or collage materials. Alternatively, they can be designed in the way of stage 'flats' and simply painted. The imitation fire for the trial and beach scenes can be made with strong brown card, and red and yellow cellophane paper.

PUPILS' WORK

The children might be encouraged to write their own verses to some of the songs. There are a number of places where pupils' own work can be incorporated, including the making of the friezes, items to be placed on the collage, signs, paper fish for the beach scene, and so on.

THE PLAY

The story for the play is based on the narratives in the Gospels of Luke and John. Where the actual words from the Bible are used, they are taken from the Contemporary English Version.

THE NATIONAL FRAMEWORK FOR RELIGIOUS EDUCATION

At the Foundation Stage, the play contributes to the following early learning goals identified in the Framework:

* Personal, social and emotional development
* Communication, language and literacy
* Knowledge and understanding of the world
* Creative development

At Key Stage One, the play contributes to many of the requirements, especially:

1b name and explore a range of celebrations, worship and rituals in religion.

1d explore how religious beliefs and ideas can be expressed through the arts.

2a reflect on and consider religious and spiritual feelings, experiences and concepts such as worship, wonder, praise, thanks, concern, joy and sadness.

2d reflect on how spiritual and moral values relate to their own behaviour.

3f story: how and why some stories are sacred and important in religion.

3g celebrations: how and why celebrations are important in religion.

3n using their senses.

3o using art and design, music, dance and drama to develop their creative talents and imagination.

OUR EASTER PLAY SCRIPT

BIBLE LINK

The story is taken from Luke 22:7–20 and 39–62; John 13:3–9; Luke 23:38 and 47; John 20:1–8; John 21:1–17.

This play follows the events of Maundy Thursday, Good Friday and Easter Day as seen through the eyes of Jesus' disciple, Peter. The drama is carried by the story narrative, which needs to be read by an adult. If required, it is possible to draw the lines given to the cast members back into the main narrative so that the children enact the drama without speaking parts.

No props or scenery are required for the stage area other than where indicated in the script.

Cast

(In order of appearance)
Adult narrator
Peter (speaking part)
Jesus (speaking part)
John
Man carrying a jar of water
Passover crowd
Other disciples
Crowd for garden of Gethsemane
Woman who recognises Peter (speaking part)
Small group round fire
Mary Magdalene

Props

(Earthenware) jar of water
Low table
Bread (for the foot-washing scene and the beach scene)
Wine
Towel
Bowl
Large wooden cross or picture of an empty cross
A piece of purple fabric
Sign printed with the words 'This is the King of the Jews'
CD player (for Easter music)
Imitation fire (for trial scene and beach scene)
Frieze or collage of the Easter garden, showing the tomb with the stone rolled away
A large fishing net
Paper fish hidden inside a large plain paper bag (for fish template, see page 28)

Narrator: This is the story of a young man called Peter. Peter used to be a fisherman until, one special day, he became one of Jesus' friends. That was three years before our story begins. Today, Peter wants to tell you what happened at the time we now know as Easter. It all began with Passover. The Passover festival is one of the most important celebrations in the Jewish year. Everyone wants to be in Jerusalem for Passover and the city is always crowded with people. Peter and Jesus' other friends were wondering what Jesus wanted to do about preparing for the special Passover meal. But, as usual, Jesus had it all planned.

Jesus and Peter enter the stage.

Jesus: Go and prepare the Passover meal for us to eat.
Peter: Where do you want us to prepare it?'
Jesus: As you go into the city, you will meet a man carrying a jar of water. Follow him into the house. The owner will take you upstairs and show you a large room. Prepare the meal there.

Jesus and Peter exit. The children playing the Passover crowd come on to the stage. In the middle of them is the man (child) carrying the jar of water. John and Peter enter and push through the crowd. They follow the man carrying the jar of water slowly around the stage as the song is sung by all.

SONG 1

Follow the man

(Tune: Here we go round the mulberry bush)

Follow the man with the water jar,
The water jar, the water jar,
Follow the man with the water jar,
On Passover Day in the morning.

Don't lose the man with the water jar,
The water jar, the water jar,
Don't lose the man with the water jar,
On Passover Day in the morning.

Push your way through all the crowds,
All the crowds, all the crowds,
Push your way through all the crowds,
On Passover Day in the morning.

Up the stairs to prepare the feast,
Prepare the feast, prepare the feast.
Up the stairs to prepare the feast,
For Passover in the evening.

At the end of the song, the crowd and water carrier leave the stage. Peter and John get ready for the Passover meal. The low table is brought on to the stage. Peter and John put bread and wine on the table. Nearby they place the towel and bowl.

Narrator: Later that day, Jesus and the others came to the house where Peter and John had prepared the meal.

Jesus and other disciples enter the stage and sit down.

Narrator: During the meal, Jesus did an amazing thing. He stood up and tied a towel around his waist. Then he filled a bowl with water and knelt in front of each one of his friends. Slowly and carefully he washed everyone's feet. Well, you can imagine what their feet were like with all the dust from the roads. It was a job for a servant—not for God's Son.

SONG 2

The foot washing song

(Tune: Ring-a-ring of roses)

During the following song, Jesus enacts the foot-washing.

Reproduced with permission from *Our Easter Play* published by BRF 2009 (978 1 84101 466 1)

Sing a song of toeses,
Our feet don't smell like roses,
A-tishoo! A-tishoo,
Walking up and down.

Sing a song of toeses,
It makes us hold our noses.
A-tishoo! A-tishoo,
Walking up and down.

In the water sploshes
Each foot Jesus washes.
A-tishoo! A-tishoo,
We've been in town.

Do it for each other,
Your sister and your brother.
Remember, remember,
For everyone around.

Narrator: When Jesus reached Peter, Peter stopped him.

Peter: Lord, are you going to wash my feet?

Jesus: If I don't wash you, you don't really belong to me.

Narrator: Peter couldn't say 'no'. He looked at Jesus and said…

Peter: Lord, don't just wash my feet. Wash my hands and my head, too!

SONG 2 (REPRISE)

The foot washing song

(Tune: Ring-a-ring of roses)

During the last verse, Jesus sits down again, in between the disciples.

Do it for each other,
Your sister and your brother.
Remember, remember,
For everyone around.

Jesus holds up the bread and wine and passes it to the disciples. This should be done with reverence.

Narrator: During the meal, Jesus shared some bread and some wine with all his friends. He told them that they should continue to share bread and wine in the same way, as it would help them to remember him in years to come. Today, one of the names for this special meal is Holy Communion.

Jesus leads the disciples off stage. The table, bread, wine, bowl and towel are cleared from the stage. Jesus and his disciples return and kneel down.

Narrator: When the meal was finished, Jesus and his friends left the house. They followed Jesus across the city to one of his favourite places. It was a quiet garden on the Mount of Olives. Jesus often went there to pray and that's what he did now.

After a silent pause, the children enact the following scene.

Narrator: After an hour or so, a crowd of people burst into the garden. Jesus was taken away by the people who had come to arrest him. Peter followed them from a distance until they arrived at the high priest's house.

A crowd comes on and Jesus is led off in one direction while the disciples run off in the other. Peter comes back on to the stage and cautiously follows Jesus from a distance. Once Peter has exited, the imitation fire is placed in the centre of the stage. After a small pause, Peter comes on stage and stands by the fire. The woman and a small group come on stage and, like Peter, warm their hands around the fire. Peter, the woman and a small group enact the following scene as it is narrated.

Narrator: In the garden was a fire. As it was a cold night, Peter sat by the fire to warm his hands. One of the women around the fire pointed her finger at him.

Woman: This man was with Jesus!

Reproduced with permission from *Our Easter Play* published by BRF 2009 (978 1 84101 466 1)

Peter: No, I wasn't!

Narrator: But she kept telling people that Peter was a friend of Jesus. Three times Peter told them that he didn't know Jesus. Then, suddenly, Peter heard a cockerel crowing nearby. When he heard the sound, he remembered that he had promised Jesus he would never let him down. Peter looked up and saw Jesus looking at him. Jesus knew what Peter had done. Peter left the fire and went outside. He cried hard when he realised that he had let Jesus down.

Peter runs off stage in one direction. The woman and others exit the stage on the opposite side. The imitation fire is removed from the stage.

One of the following songs or hymns, or any other suitable song, may be sung at this point in the drama.

- Lord of the dance (*Come and Praise* 22)
- When Jesus walked in Galilee (*Come and Praise* 25)
- There is a green hill far away

During the song, either a wooden cross or a large picture of an empty cross is placed or hung on the stage. The cross is draped with a piece of purple fabric, and the words 'This is the King of the Jews' are placed above it. There are no children on the stage for the following narration or during the playing of the Easter music.

Narrator: On the day we call Good Friday, Jesus was taken through the streets of Jerusalem to a hill outside the city. There he was nailed to a cross. Above his head was hung a sign that read, 'This is the King of the Jews'. After six hours, Jesus died. When he did so, the Roman soldier in charge said, 'Jesus must really have been a good man!'

Some appropriate Easter music is played—for example, the Easter Hymn from Cavalleria Rusticana *by Mascagni, the Hallelujah Chorus from Handel's* Messiah, *or any other suitable piece. There is a short silence as the music finishes. The cross is then quietly removed from the stage.*

Narrator: It was early on Sunday morning when Mary Magdalene brought Jesus' friends the news.

The frieze or collage of the Easter garden scene is displayed on stage. Mary walks slowly on to the stage.

Narrator: On that first Easter morning, Mary had gone to the place where Jesus was buried. When she got there, she found the huge stone covering the doorway had been moved. She ran back to tell the others the news.

Mary runs off stage.

SONG 3

The race

(Tune: Three blind mice)

Sing the song three times, each time getting faster. As the song is sung, Peter and John race the full length of the hall and on to the stage to the empty tomb.

Peter and John,
Peter and John,
See how they run,
See how they run.
They run to look inside the tomb,
They strain their eyes in the dark and gloom,
John stays out, Peter enters the room.
But Jesus is gone!

Narrator: John and Peter ran as fast as they could. John got there first, but it was Peter who went inside. There was no

Reproduced with permission from *Our Easter Play* published by BRF 2009 (978 1 84101 466 1)

one there—the tomb was empty! It was then that they remembered what Jesus had told them. Jesus had said that after three days he would come back to life again. Peter and John could hardly believe it! Wondering what had happened, they returned to the others.

Peter and John exit, shaking their heads and looking perplexed. The Easter garden scene is removed from the stage.

Narrator: Jesus' friends were very frightened. They gathered together in a room and locked the door. But Jesus proved that he had come back to life in a new and very special way. Even though the door was locked, he came and stood among them. He reassured them, ate with them and spoke with them. As the days went on, Jesus continued to show the disciples that he really had come back to life. One day, there was a very special moment for Peter. It was the day when Peter and some of the others went fishing.

The frieze or collage of the lake scene is displayed on stage. Peter and six other disciples enter, carrying the net. One person discreetly carries the bag containing the fish. The seven disciples follow the actions as described in the verses of the song. Jesus enters the stage at the appropriate moment in the song, but stands apart from the others. After the line 'They'll be full to bursting!' the bag is opened and the fish tipped into the net.

SONG 4

The fishing song

(Tune: What shall we do with the drunken sailor?)

What shall we do on this fine evening?
What shall we do on this fine evening?
What shall we do on this fine evening?
We'll be going fishing.

All night long we let our nets down,
All night long we let our nets down,
All night long we let our nets down,
But all we've caught is nothing.

Tired and hungry, we've got no breakfast,
Tired and hungry, we've got no breakfast,
Tired and hungry, we've got no breakfast,
Early in the morning.

Who's that standing on the seashore?
Who's that standing on the seashore?
Who's that standing on the seashore?
Is it really Jesus?

Throw your nets out on the right side,
Throw your nets out on the right side,
Throw your nets out on the right side,
They'll be full to bursting!

Bread and fish for our breakfast,
Bread and fish for our breakfast,
Bread and fish for our breakfast
On the beach with Jesus.

The imitation fire is placed on the stage and everyone sits down around it. Jesus fetches the bread and gives each person in the group of disciples some bread and fish. Then the main group remain by the fire while Jesus leads Peter to one side.

Narrator: After breakfast, Jesus took Peter to one side. As they walked along the seashore, Jesus asked Peter a question.

Jesus: Peter, do you love me?

Peter: Yes, Lord, you know I do!

Narrator: Three times Jesus asked Peter the same question. Three times Peter answered, 'Yes, Lord, you know I love you!' Then Peter remembered that awful night when he had said three times that he didn't know Jesus. Jesus and Peter stopped walking. Jesus turned and looked at Peter. 'Follow me!' he said.

Jesus exits the stage, while Peter looks on.

Narrator: Jesus' disciples told everyone the good news of what had happened on that first Easter Day. As the good news spread, so more and more people came to hear about Jesus and believe in him. Still today, the message is being passed on. Still today, the good news of Easter is celebrated all over the world.

Peter returns to the other disciples in the group. They are then joined by the whole cast. If there are too many children for the stage, some may flow out into the hall.

SONG 4

The fishing song (final verse)

(Tune: What shall we do with the drunken sailor?)

Jesus is our friend for ever,
Jesus is our friend for ever,
Jesus is our friend for ever,
Come and follow Jesus!

All the children enact passing the message on. The final verse is repeated as everyone leaves the stage and continues until all have exited.

THE END

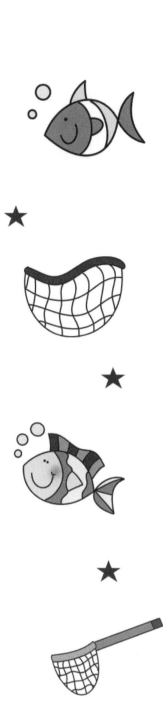

Reproduced with permission from *Our Easter Play* published by BRF 2009 (978 1 84101 466 1)

APPENDIX ONE

OUR EASTER PLAY SONG LYRICS

FOLLOW THE MAN

(Tune: Here we go round the mulberry bush)

Follow the man with the water jar,
The water jar, the water jar,
Follow the man with the water jar,
On Passover Day in the morning.

Don't lose the man with the water jar,
The water jar, the water jar,
Don't lose the man with the water jar,
On Passover Day in the morning.

Push your way through all the crowds,
All the crowds, all the crowds,
Push your way through all the crowds,
On Passover Day in the morning.

Up the stairs to prepare the feast,
Prepare the feast, prepare the feast.
Up the stairs to prepare the feast,
For Passover in the evening.

THE FOOT WASHING SONG

(Tune: Ring-a-ring of roses)

Sing a song of toeses,
Our feet don't smell like roses,
A-tishoo! A-tishoo,
Walking up and down.

Sing a song of toeses,
It makes us hold our noses.
A-tishoo! A-tishoo,
Walking up and down.

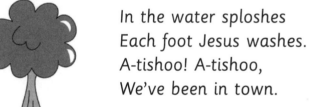

In the water sploshes
Each foot Jesus washes.
A-tishoo! A-tishoo,
We've been in town.

Do it for each other,
Your sister and your brother.
Remember, remember,
For everyone around.

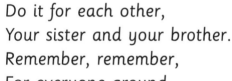

Song 3

THE RACE

(Tune: Three blind mice)

Peter and John,
Peter and John,
See how they run,
See how they run.
They run to look inside the tomb,
They strain their eyes in the dark and gloom,
John stays out, Peter enters the room.
But Jesus is gone!

Song 4

THE FISHING SONG

(Tune: What shall we do with the drunken sailor?)

What shall we do on this fine evening?
What shall we do on this fine evening?
What shall we do on this fine evening?
We'll be going fishing.

All night long we let our nets down,
All night long we let our nets down,
All night long we let our nets down,
But all we've caught is nothing.

Tired and hungry, we've got no breakfast,
Tired and hungry, we've got no breakfast,
Tired and hungry, we've got no breakfast,
Early in the morning.

Who's that standing on the seashore?
Who's that standing on the seashore?
Who's that standing on the seashore?
Is it really Jesus?

Throw your nets out on the right side,
Throw your nets out on the right side,
Throw your nets out on the right side,
They'll be full to bursting!

Bread and fish for our breakfast,
Bread and fish for our breakfast,
Bread and fish for our breakfast
On the beach with Jesus.

Jesus is our friend for ever,
Jesus is our friend for ever,
Jesus is our friend for ever,
Come and follow Jesus!

APPENDIX TWO

OUR EASTER PLAY MUSIC NOTATION

Song 1

FOLLOW
THE MAN

(Tune: Here we go round the mulberry bush)

Song 2

THE FOOT WASHING SONG

(Tune: Ring-a-ring of roses)

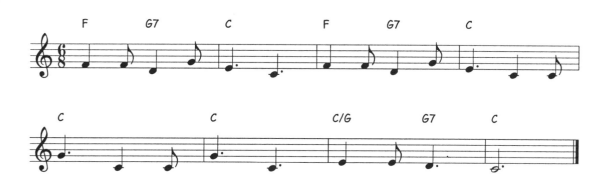

23

Song 3

THE RACE

(Tune: Three blind mice)

Song 4

THE FISHING SONG

(Tune: What shall we do with the drunken sailor?)

Reproduced with permission from *Our Easter Play* published by BRF 2009 (978 1 84101 466 1)

APPENDIX THREE

CRAFT TEMPLATE

FISH TEMPLATE

Also by Brian Ogden

NURSERY RHYME NATIVITIES

Three easy-to-perform plays for pre-school and early years learning

One of the biggest problems faced by those working with very young children at Christmas is how to involve pre-readers in the nativity story with the minimum of fuss and manageable preparation.

Here is an ideal solution that will delight teachers and parents alike. In this book, popular author Brian Ogden offers three very diverse plays—all of which can be performed with groups of any size. Each one tells the story of the first Christmas from a different perspective, using well-known nursery rhyme tunes to bring the storyline to life. Simple directions, costumes and props ensure that the children are given the opportunity to participate fully in the performance.

Includes photocopy permission.

ISBN 978 1 84101 236 0   £7.99
Available direct from BRF/Barnabas using the order form opposite,
or visit www.barnabasinschools.org.uk

ORDERFORM

REF	TITLE		PRICE	QTY	TOTAL
236 0	Nursery Rhyme Nativities		£7.99		
		Postage and packing			
		Donation			
		TOTAL			

POSTAGE AND PACKING CHARGES

Order value	UK	Europe	Surface	Air Mail
£7.00 & under	£1.25	£3.00	£3.50	£5.50
£7.10–£30.00	£2.25	£5.50	£6.50	£10.00
Over £30.00	FREE	prices on request		

Name _____ Account Number _____

Address _____

_____ Postcode _____

Telephone Number_____

Email _____

Payment by: ❑ Cheque ❑ Mastercard ❑ Visa ❑ Postal Order ❑ Maestro

Card no ⬜⬜⬜⬜ ⬜⬜⬜⬜ ⬜⬜⬜⬜ ⬜⬜⬜⬜ ⬜⬜⬜

Valid from ⬜⬜⬜⬜ Expires ⬜⬜⬜⬜ Issue no. ⬜⬜⬜

Security code* ⬜⬜⬜ *Last 3 digits on the reverse of the card.
ESSENTIAL IN ORDER TO PROCESS YOUR ORDER

Shaded boxes for Maestro use only

Signature _____ Date _____

All orders must be accompanied by the appropriate payment.

Please send your completed order form to:

BRF, 15 The Chambers, Vineyard, Abingdon OX14 3FE
Tel. 01865 319700 / Fax. 01865 319701 Email: enquiries@brf.org.uk

❑ Please send me further information about BRF publications.

Available from your local Christian bookshop.　　　　　BRF is a Registered Charity

Resourcing **Collective Worship and Assemblies, RE, Festivals, Drama** and **Art** in primary schools

- Barnabas RE Days—exploring Christianity creatively
- INSET
- Books and resources
- www.barnabasinschools.org.uk

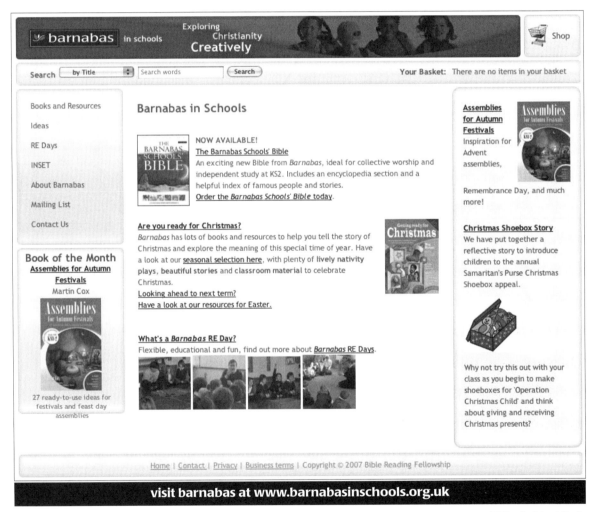

Have you signed up to receive the Barnabas monthly email?

To receive mailings about *Barnabas* resources and services, sign up at:

www.barnabasinschools.org.uk